Peter Leigh

Published in association with
The Basic Skills Agency

Hodder & Stoughton
A MEMBER OF THE HODDER HEADLINE GROUP

Orders: please contact Bookpoint Ltd, 39 Milton Park, Abingdon, Oxon
OX14 4TD. Telephone: (44) 01235 400414, Fax: (44) 01235 400454. Lines are
open from 9.00 - 6.00, Monday to Saturday, with a 24 hour message answering
service. Email address: orders@bookpoint.co.uk

British Library Cataloguing in Publication Data
A catalogue record for this title is available from The British Library

ISBN 0 340 73817 0

First published 1995
Impression number 10 9 8 7 6 5 4 3 2 1
Year   2004 2003 2002 2001 2000 1999 1998

Typeset by Transet Limited, Coventry, England.
Printed in Great Britain for Hodder & Stoughton Educational, a division of
Hodder Headline Plc, 338 Euston Road, London, NW1 3BH by
Athenaeum Press Ltd, Gateshead, Tyne & Wear.

1
......

Paul decided that he wanted to die. Right then. At that very moment.

He lay down in the tent, and decided that he would lay there forever. He would never move again.

Through the opening of the tent, he could see Johnny. Johnny was starting to shave himself in the wing mirror of his motorbike. 'Before I die,' thought Paul, 'I shall strangle Johnny.'

'Let's go down to Portonsea for the weekend,' Johnny had said.

'Let's go camping,' Johnny had said.

'We can earn a few quid picking potatoes,' Johnny had said.

And Paul had said, 'Good idea!' And now he wanted to die. He had spent four hours picking potatoes. He had earned £6.59 after tax, and now he wanted to die. He felt as if he had been roasted in a hot oven, and then jumped on by a mad cow.

Johnny looked at himself in the mirror. 'There's no doubt about it,' he said. 'You are gorgeous. Some little girl's going to be lucky tonight.' He looked across at the tent. 'Come on Paul! Get a move on!'

Paul groaned.

Johnny poked his head into the tent. 'What's the matter? Don't like the hard work, do we? Don't like getting our hands dirty? Oh, poor little boy! What you need is a breath of fresh air...' He grabbed Paul's ankles, and pulled him out of the tent.

'You can't do this to me,' said Paul feebly. 'I'm dying.' But he could, and did.

'And now a cold shower!' He picked up the bowl of shaving water, and emptied it over Paul's head.

Paul just moaned a little louder. 'I'm crippled. Crippled for life!' Johnny hauled him to his

feet. 'One day,' said Paul, 'one day I shall have my revenge.'

'You'll be lucky,' said Johnny. 'Just get cleaned up. Then we can go.'

Paul found a bowl and some water, and somehow managed to get himself washed and changed, and his hair combed. He put on his crash helmet, and climbed on to the back of Johnny's bike.

'Why do I do these things?' said Paul.

'Because without me, your life would be nothing!' said Johnny, and they roared off.

2

Portonsea was a small seaside town – one disco, two pubs, and ten amusement arcades. Everywhere smelt of chips.

Johnny and Paul parked outside the disco.

'Here we are then, Paul. Portonsea! Is Portonsea ready for me, I ask myself? Can Portonsea take me? I can hear them whispering already. "Who is that handsome bloke?" they are saying. "Is he on the tele?" they are saying.'

'"Is he on drugs?" they are saying,' said Paul.

'It's just my raw, male sex appeal. They can smell it.'

'I thought that was your aftershave!'

Johnny ran up the steps to the disco. Paul hobbled after. A man in an evening suit stepped in front of them.

'Sorry lads! You can't come in!'

'What?'

'You can't come in. Smart clothes only.
No leathers!'

'What? These are smart!'

'Sorry! Club rule. Jacket and tie only.'

'Look, it's just plain leather. There's no
razor-blades sewn in the cuffs or anything.'

'Sorry!'

'All we want is a drink and a dance.
We won't wreck the place.'

'I've already told you! It's club rules!
Now off you go!' Two other men stepped
out of the shadows behind him.

'Quick Paul,' said Johnny. 'Phone the zoo.
Someone's left the cages open.'

The men moved forwards.

'Come on Johnny. Let's find somewhere else.'
Paul took Johnny's arm, and eased him
down the steps. But Johnny was angry.

'I bet your wife really loves it when you talk tough,' he shouted. 'I expect she prefers little men.'

Paul hurried Johnny along the street. He was still shouting back at the men. There was a pub a few doors down.

'Come on Johnny! Let's go in here for a drink.' He pushed Johnny through the door, and sat him down. Then Paul went to the bar for the drinks, and that was when he saw her.

3

......

She was sitting in the room on the other
side of the bar. She was with some
friends talking and laughing. And she
looked just right. So fresh and natural.
Paul couldn't help staring. She looked
so nice.

A crowd came into the other room.
Paul couldn't see her anymore. He
shifted sideways along the bar,
and crouched down beside the wall.
He could just see her between two men.
She was telling a story, and she was
laughing and clapping her hands.
She had such lovely hands. Lovely
and delicate hands. She was so
fine, so good. Paul felt himself
grinning. He could have watched
her there all night.

She looked up, and for a moment
her eyes caught his. She had dark
eyes. Dark and deep eyes. Eyes
that you wanted to look into. Eyes
that you could tell things to. Important

things. Not the things he spoke to
Johnny about. But private things.
Things he had never told anyone else.

He was suddenly aware of a silence
around him. Three men with tattoos
on their arms were looking at him.
He was crouched beneath the dartboard.

'Oh sorry!' said Paul, and moved quickly
out of the way. He sat down again
next to Johnny.

'Well?' said Johnny.

'Well what?'

'Where are they then?'

'Where are what?'

'The drinks!'

'Drinks?'

'Yes! Drinks! D-R-I-N-K-S! Drinks!
What you get in a pub. What we
came in here for. What you went to the
bar for. And what I'm still waiting for.'

'Oh... right... yes... drinks. Er... sorry! I forgot.'

'Forgot?'

'Well, that is... I was distracted.'

'Distracted?'

'Yes.'

'Distracted by what?'

'Well... I... er... I saw this girl.'

'Girl? What girl?'

'Oh... just a girl. In the other bar there.'

'Oh I see! You get one glimpse of a girl,
and that's my drink! One flash of skirt,
and you're a great wobbling blob
of jelly! Never mind the really important
things in life like my drink. Never
mind the fact that I need a drink, that
I am desperate for a drink. Never mind
the fact that it's my bike that brought you
here, and that it's my tent that
you'll be sleeping in.'

'Yes... well... I'm sorry.' There was a pause.

'What's she like then?'

'What?'

'What's she like, this girl of yours?'

'Oh, she's really nice. She's...'

'Well, let's have a look at her then!'
Johnny jumped up. Paul tried to stop
him, but it was too late. He followed
Johnny to the bar.

'Where is she then?'

'She's just over there. She...' Paul's voice
trailed off. There was just an empty
table with a few glasses on it.

'But... but she was there! She was
there just a few minutes ago!'

'Well she's not there now.'

'But I saw her! She must have gone!'

'I'm not surprised. One look at you is
enough for any girl!'

'But she can only just have gone. Let's see
if we can find her.'

'I'm not moving from here till I've had
a drink.'

'Oh, come on Johnny!'

'Come on nothing. I'm not chasing after
any girl till I've had a drink. You go
by yourself.'

Paul stood still for a moment, and then
dashed out.

But it was no good! There was no-one
about. He had missed her. He wandered
about the car park for a bit, and then
came back in. He bought himself a drink,
and sat down next to Johnny. 'Well that's it,'
he thought. 'I'll never see her again.'

4
......

But he did see her again. The very next day.

He had spent a miserable evening in the pub,
and then had tossed and turned
in his sleeping bag all night. In the
morning he came back into Portonsea
with Johnny just for something to do.

They wandered up and down looking
at the shops. Paul stood idly by a
chemist's and Johnny crossed the road
to look at a gift shop. A shop assistant
put something in the window of the
chemist's, and something about her hands
caught Paul's eye. Lovely, delicate hands. Paul
caught his breath. She was wearing a white
coat. In the lapel was a badge. It said 'Sandra'.
She stood up, and for a moment Paul looked
again into her eyes. Dark eyes. Then
she was gone.

Paul flew over the road, just missing being
run over. Johnny was still looking in the
window of the gift shop.

'I've just seen her again!'

'Seen who?'

'That girl.'

'What girl?'

'The girl I told you about. You know.
In the pub.'

'Oh, her!'

'Yes, her! Well, I've just seen her again.'

'Poor girl. I bet she thought she was
rid of you.'

'She works in the chemist's over there.
Her name's Sandra.'

'Sandra?'

'Yes.'

'How do you know that?'

'It's got it on her coat. Look, there she is.'

The door of the chemist's opened, and
Sandra came out. She was clutching
some money tightly in her hand. Her coat
was unbuttoned and blew out behind her.
She tripped lightly down the street,
and disappeared into the next shop. Paul let
his breath out slowly.

'Look at that. Isn't she great? She must have
gone to get some change.'

'You've no chance!'

'What?'

'You've no chance. Forget it. Go home!'

'What do you mean? Why not?'

'Well, she's almost good-looking. That puts
her way out of your league!'

'Oh, shut up! Look, there she is again.'

Sandra came out into the street. She was
so light and lovely. Paul felt himself
begin to grin like last night. She was so...
There was a shout from next to him.

'Yoo-hoo! Sandra! Coo-ee! Sandra!
Have you got some condoms for my mate
here? He really fancies you, and...'

Johnny didn't say any more. He couldn't
with his head in an armlock, and Paul's
hand clamped over his mouth.

'Shut up, you idiot!' hissed Paul. 'Shut up!'
He held Johnny until he was quiet,
and then let him up. 'You great prat! What
are you trying to do? Ruin everything?'

Sandra had gone. Johnny was laughing.
'I was giving you a helping hand.'

'A helping hand? You call that a helping
hand?'

'Well, you're the shy type. She needs to know
you fancy her.'

'Oh, thanks a bunch! And condoms?
Condoms, I ask you! What's she going to
think of me now?'

'She's going to think you're very caring.
Caring and considerate. Thoughtful and

protective. Sensitive to her every
need. A new man!'

'Oh, get lost!'

'All right then, lover boy. See you later!
Don't mind him, lady,' he said to a passing
shopper, 'he's just in love.' And off he strolled.

'That's Johnny for you,' thought Paul. Friends!

5

Paul stood outside the chemist's shop.
He had walked past it three times now.
He just had to go in. Suppose Sandra
had heard. She would think he was
a yob. He couldn't let her think he was a yob.
But what could he say? 'I'm sorry about
my mate, Sandra, but...' 'Allow me to
apologise for the behaviour of my friend,
Sandra, but...' And he couldn't just call her
'Sandra'. 'Excuse me, Miss...' No, that was
even worse. They all sounded stupid. He
would just have to do the best he could. He
clenched his fists, took a deep breath, and
with his heart thumping, opened the door.

A bell tinkled as he closed the door
behind him. There was a queue of three
or four women. Sandra was serving.
Paul stood quietly at the back, and watched
her wrapping up the little packets
and bottles. When she bent over the till,
her hair fell forwards over her face,
and she smoothed it back, and she had
such a slim wrist. And for each customer
she had a word and a smile. And when

she reached up for something and stood
on tip-toe, he could see the whole
shape of her...

'Yes, young man? What can I do for you?'

...And when she bent down, he could see the
curve of her neck and, oh, a glimpse of her...

'I said what can I do for you?'

Paul jerked round. Another woman
in a white coat had come out of the back,
and was looking at him.

'For the third time, young man, what do
you want?' The other women laughed.

'He doesn't want you, Betty! He wants young
Sandra here. He can't keep his eyes off
her. He's been gawping at her ever
since he came in.' There was more laughter.

'Well?' she said again. Sandra kept
her head down.

Paul looked round wildly. 'A packet of tissues
please.'

'Do you want regular or mansize?'

'Oh! mansize, Betty! Give him mansize!
He'll need mansize!' More laughter.

Paul threw some money on the counter,
grabbed the tissues, and ran. As he
reached the door, he turned back.
Sandra looked up at him. Her eyes gleamed.
Then he was through the door and out!

6
......

Paul paced up and down a side street
near the chemist's. He still had the box
of tissues in his hand. What a fool!
What a drongo! And what must she think?
He groaned to himself. Even if he saw her
again what could he say?

He peered round the corner. The church
clock struck one, and even as he looked,
the blind came down behind the chemist's
door. Lunch time! Perhaps Sandra went
home for her dinner! He peeked again,
and saw Sandra come out of the shop,
and close the door behind her. She was
still wearing her white coat.

He jumped back, and leant against the wall,
and tried to control his breathing. This was it!
His last chance! He could hear footsteps
coming closer. He would have to time
this perfectly. He had to get it just right.
The footsteps were getting closer. Not yet...
not yet... nearly... Now! Paul stepped out,
walked round the corner, straight into one of
the women from the chemist's.

She grunted, and shopping went everywhere.

'Oh God, I'm sorry!' said Paul. There were oranges rolling all over the pavement. Paul went down on his knees, and tried to gather them together. A pair of slim legs walked up, paused, and skipped by on the outside. Paul grabbed everything he could, and stuffed it into the woman's bag. She was going on about young people these days, and Paul kept saying, 'I'm sorry! I'm sorry!' He pushed the last orange into her bag. The white coat was just disappearing round a bend. Paul just pelted after it.

7

......

Just round the bend, he caught up with her. 'Look,' he said, 'I'm sorry!'

'Oh!' she said, and carried on walking.

'Yes, I am. I'm really sorry.'

'What are you sorry about?'

'Back there at the chemist's.'

'Oh, that's all right. Don't mind them. They were just having a bit of fun.' Her voice was light and easy, almost mocking.
 'How's the cold?'

'The cold?'

'Yes.' Paul looked blank. 'The tissues.' She nodded at his hand. Paul looked, and saw the box of tissues still stuck in it.

'Oh... oh... I haven't got a cold. I needed the tissues for... for... for... something else.' He stuffed them into his other hand.

'Oh good. I'm glad.'

'Glad?'

'Yes, glad. Do you always repeat what everyone else says.'

'Oh... no... I'm sorry.'

'You keep saying that too.'

'About my friend I mean. Shouting out like that.'

'You don't have to apologise for your friend.'

'Oh... no... He's all right really. In fact he's great. Once you get to know him.'

'I'm glad to hear it.'

Sandra had stopped, and was looking at Paul. Paul looked back at her. He could have looked back at her all afternoon.

'I live up here,' she said.

'Oh right,' he said. 'That's all right. I was going this way myself. I need to go along here.'

'But it's a cul-de-sac.'

'Oh right... yes... well...' Paul looked round desperately. There were some workmen digging up the road. 'I need to look in the drains.'

'The drains?'

'Yes, I'm... er... interested in drains. And sewers. Things like that.'

'You're interested in sewers?'

'Yes... they're very... interesting. How are yours?'

'Mine?'

'Yes... your sewers?'

'How are my sewers?'

'Yes... and your drains?'

'They're very well, thank you.'

'Oh, good.'

Sandra stopped by a gate.

'I live here,' she said.

'Oh, right.'

'Bye then!'

'Bye!'

Paul walked on till he heard Sandra's
door close behind her. Carefully he
placed the box of tissues on the pavement.
He stood up, stepped back, and then
kicked it as hard as he could.
He sank slowly to his knees, and gently
banged his head on the ground.

'Drains!' he said.

'Sewers!' he said.

8
......

Sandra came out of her house, and started to walk back to work. She heard footsteps coming up behind her. She wasn't surprised.

'Hello again,' she said. 'Have you had an interesting time?'

'Interesting?'

'Yes, examining all the sewers. I expect you found it fascinating.'

'Yes, well...'

'I'm sure there are some really exciting sewers round here.'

'Yes... well...'

'But I suppose they're all small town sewers. You're probably more of the big city sewer type.'

'Oh... well... '

'Though mind you, I do believe the farm sewer has a lot to offer.'

'Oh!' He stopped. 'You're laughing at me.' She looked up at him. His face was wide open. The wind and sun had tanned it a little. He looked hurt.

'Well, what do you expect?' she said. '"I'm very interested in sewers!" What kind of a line is that?'

'Well, you had me all confused. I didn't know what to say... I only wanted to talk to you.'

'You're talking to me now,' she said gently. 'And you still haven't told me your name.' She looked up at him, and smiled. Paul felt his stomach turn very softly upside down.

'Paul,' he said. 'It's Paul.'

'Well, Paul,' she said, 'I'm Sandra.'

They walked on, and he told her about Johnny. He told her about the bike, the potatoes, the weekend, where he

came from, what he wanted to do. He
would have told her everything, right down
to his World Cup stickers and how he
had cried at ET, but they arrived back at the
chemist's.

'Listen Paul,' said Sandra, and he loved
the way she said it. 'I've got to go back
now. That pub you were in last night is
horrible. I usually go with some friends to the
other one. We'll be there tonight at about
eight. Why don't you come?'

'Really?' said Paul.

'Yes, really!' She opened the door of the
chemist's.

'And you noticed me last night?'

'Course I noticed you!'

'Tonight?'

'Yes!'

'At eight?'

'Yes!'

'And you want me to come?'

'YES!' And she closed the door.

Paul turned, and ran down the street,
on to the beach, right to the very end where
there was no-one else around. He stopped,
looked out to sea, and yelled at the top
of his voice.

'SHE SAID YES!'